HOME ORGANIST LIBRARY VOLUME 29

Modern Love Songs

Arranged by Kenneth Baker.

This publication is not authorised for sale in the
United States of America and/or Canada.

Wise Publications
London/New York/Paris/Sydney/Copenhagen/Madrid

Exclusive Distributors:
Music Sales Limited
8/9 Frith Street, London W1V 5TZ, England.
Music Sales Pty Limited
120 Rothschild Avenue, Rosebery, NSW 2018, Australia.

Order No. AM92371
ISBN 0-7119-4447-4
This book © Copyright 1996 by Wise Publications

Compiled by Peter Evans
Music arranged by Kenneth Baker
Music processed by MSS Studios

Book design by Studio Twenty, London
Cover illustrations with apologies to
Roy Lichtenstein

Printed in the United Kingdom by
Redwood Books Limited, Trowbridge, Wiltshire.

Your Guarantee of Quality
As publishers, we strive to produce every book to
the highest commercial standards.
The music has been freshly engraved and the book has
been carefully designed to minimise awkward page turns
and to make playing from it a real pleasure.
Particular care has been given to specifying acid-free, neutral-sized
paper made from pulps which have not been elemental chlorine bleached.
This pulp is from farmed sustainable forests and
was produced with special regard for the environment.
Throughout, the printing and binding have been planned to ensure a
sturdy, attractive publication which should give years of enjoyment.
If your copy fails to meet our high standards, please inform us
and we will gladly replace it.

Music Sales' complete catalogue describes thousands of titles and is
available in full colour sections by subject, direct from Music Sales Limited.
Please state your areas of interest and send a cheque/postal order
for £1.50 for postage to: Music Sales Limited, Newmarket Road,
Bury St. Edmunds, Suffolk IP33 3YB.

Visit the Internet Music Shop at
http://www.musicsales.co.uk

Always 70
Goodnight Girl 64
Have I Told You Lately 19
How Deep Is Your Love 78
I Believe 56
I Will Always Love You 4
If Not For You 47
Lady 16
Lay, Lady, Lay 28
Love Is All Around 74
Love So Right 60
More Than A Woman 38
My Love 44
Run To Me 10
She Believes In Me 50
Stay Another Day 68
The First Time Ever I Saw Your Face 7
Think Twice 25
Try A Little Tenderness 13
Unchained Melody 53
With You I'm Born Again 41
Woman 22
You Are So Beautiful 32
Your Song 35

I Will Always Love You

Words & Music by Dolly Parton

Upper: piano
Lower: flutes
Pedal: bass guitar
Drums: 8 beat

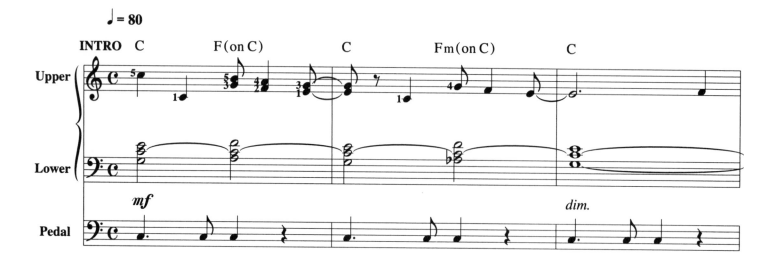

Upper: add strings　　**VERSE**

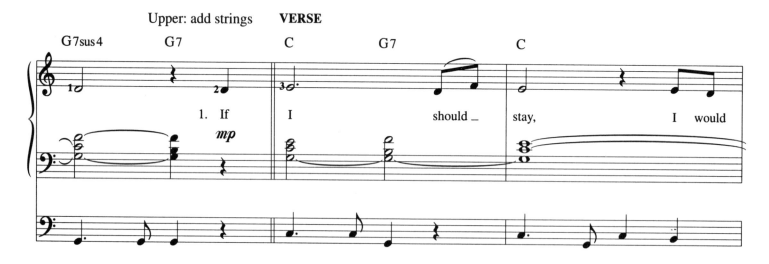

4

The First Time Ever I Saw Your Face

Words & Music by Ewan MacColl

Upper: string ensemble
Lower: flutes
Pedal: bass guitar
Drums: 8 beat

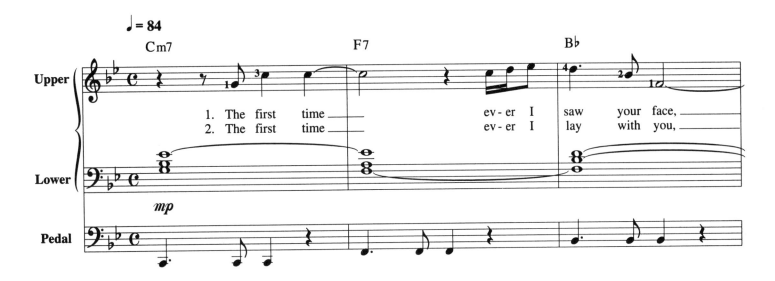

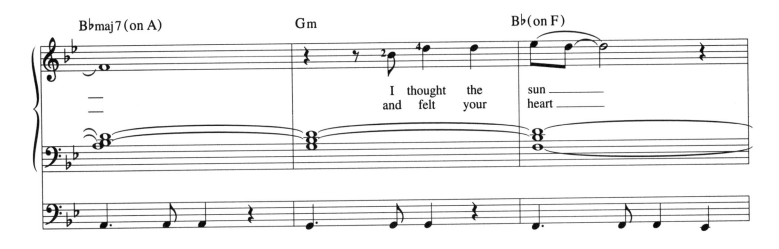

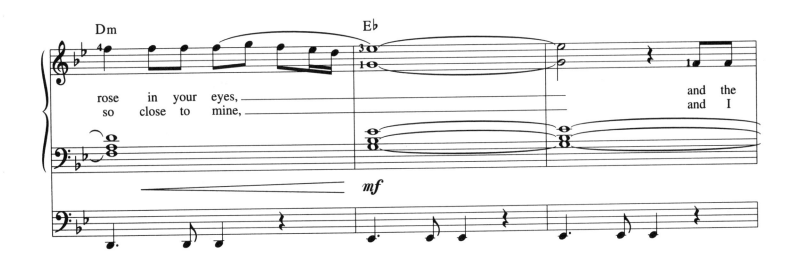

Run To Me

Words & Music by Barry Gibb, Maurice Gibb & Robin Gibb

Upper: trumpet
Lower: flutes
Pedal: bass guitar
Drums: rock

Upper: add strings

you lov - ing me. ___ Am I un - wise to o - pen up your eyes to love

CHORUS

Run to me when - ev - er you're lone - ly, run to me if
(me.)

you need a shoul - der. Now and then you'll need some - one old - er, so

dar - ling, you run to me. 2. And when you're

Upper: cut strings
VERSE

out in the cold, __ no-one be-side __ you, and no-one __ to hold,

am I un-wise to o-pen up your eyes to love me. And when you've got

no-thing to lose, __ no-thing to pay __ for, and no-thing to choose. __

Upper: add strings

D.%. and Fade

Am I un-wise to o-pen up your eyes to love

Try A Little Tenderness

Words & Music by Harry Woods, Jimmy Campbell & Reg Connelly

Upper: jazz organ
Lower: flutes + piano
Pedal: bass guitar
Drums: 8 beat

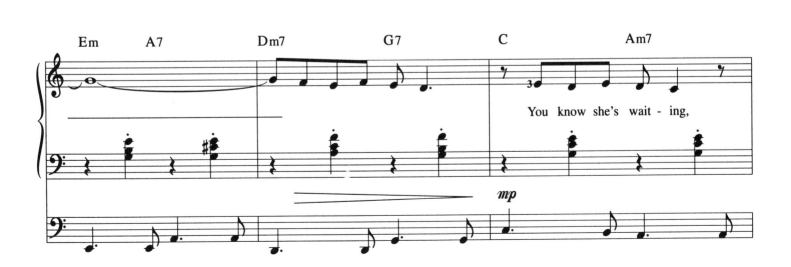

Lady

Words & Music by Lionel Richie

Upper: human voice
Lower: flutes
Pedal: bass guitar
Drums: 8 beat

I'm so lost ___ in your love. _____ And oh, we be-
long to-geth - er, won't you be-lieve ___ in my song? _____
Upper: to human voice
___ La - dy, _____ your love's the
on - ly love I need, _____ be - side me _____

Have I Told You Lately

Words & Music by Van Morrison

Upper: guitar
Lower: flutes
Pedal: 8'
Drums: 8 beat

Woman

Words & Music by John Lennon

Upper: saxophone
Lower: flutes + piano
Pedal: bass guitar
Drums: 8 beat

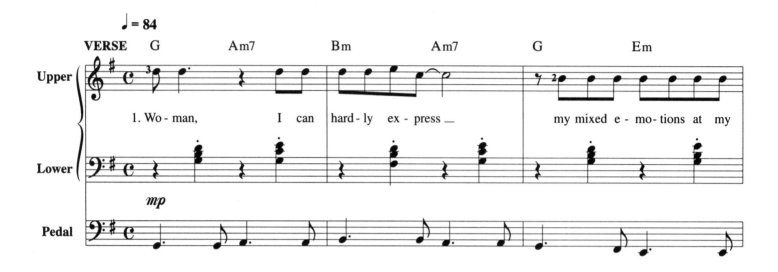

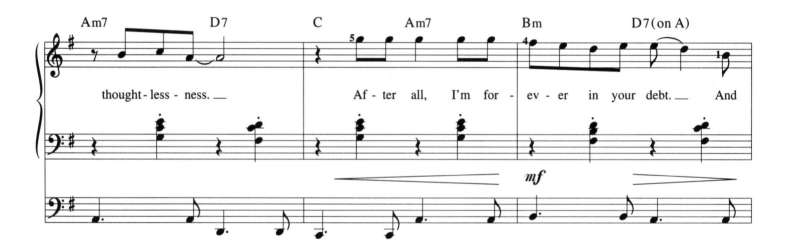

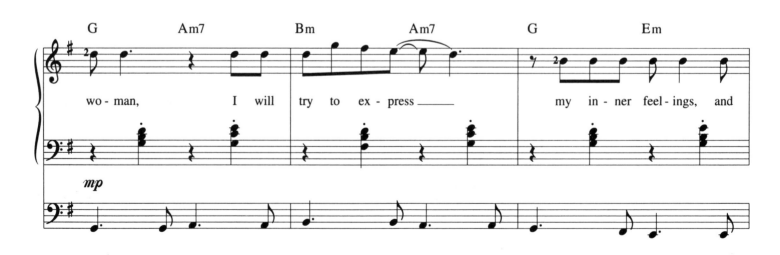

24

Think Twice

Words & Music by Andy Hill & Pete Sinfield

Upper: piano
Lower: flutes
Pedal: bass guitar
Drums: 8 beat

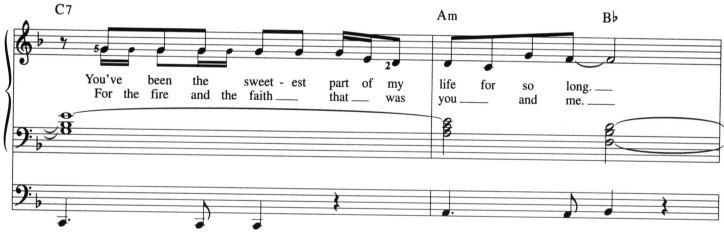

Lay, Lady, Lay

Words & Music by Bob Dylan

Upper: flute
Lower: flutes + piano
Pedal: bass guitar
Drums: 8 beat

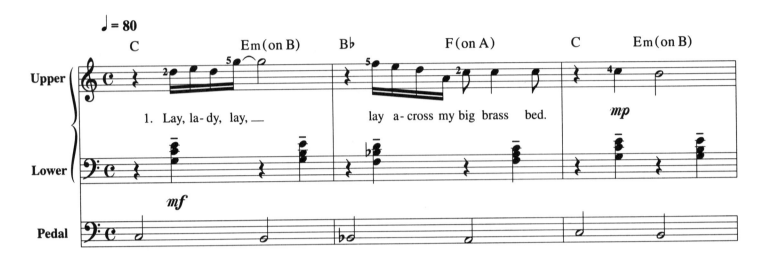

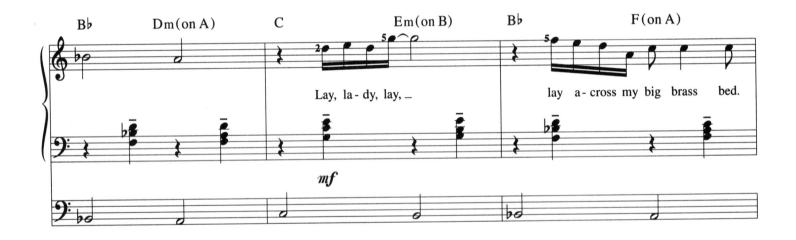

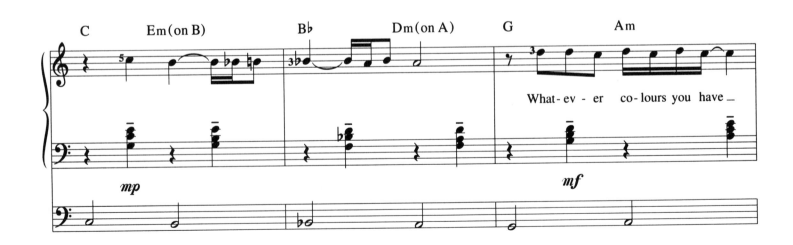

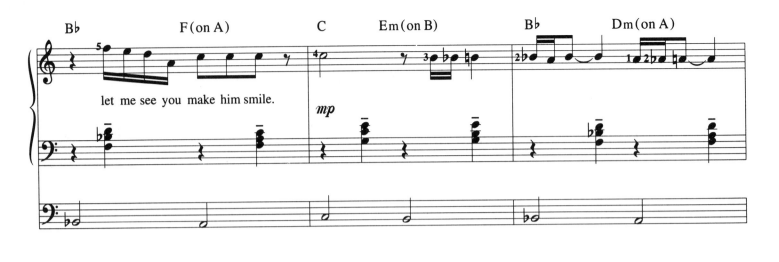

let me see you make him smile.

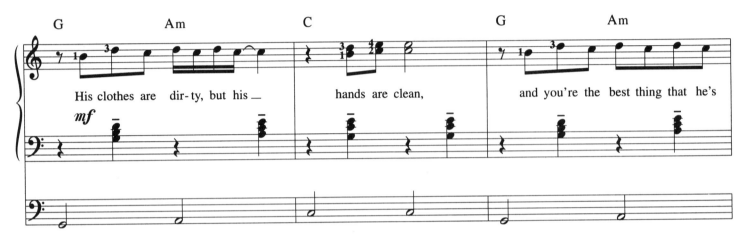

His clothes are dir-ty, but his — hands are clean, and you're the best thing that he's

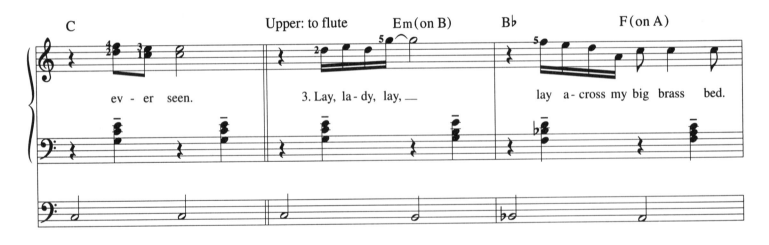

ev - er seen. 3. Lay, la - dy, lay, — lay a-cross my big brass bed.

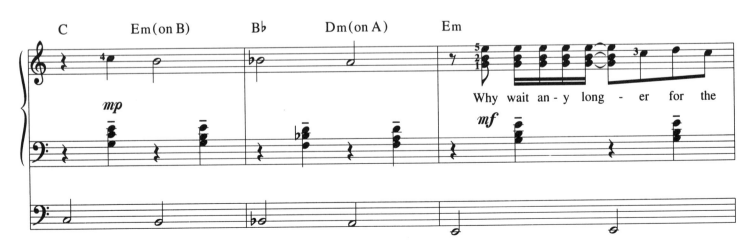

Why wait an - y long - er for the

(Repeat and Fade)

You Are So Beautiful

Words & Music by Billy Preston & Bruce Fisher

Upper: piano
Lower: flutes
Pedal: bass guitar
Drums: 8 beat

hope for,   and what's more,   you're ev-'ry-thing I   need. _____

You   are   so   beau-ti-ful,   ba-by,   to   me. _____

1.

2.

Upper: to guitar

Such   joy   and

hap-pi-ness _____   you _____   bring.   (I wan-na thank _ you, babe _____)

Your Song

Words & Music by Elton John and Bernie Taupin

Upper: human voice
Lower: flutes
Pedal: bass guitar
Drums: 8 beat

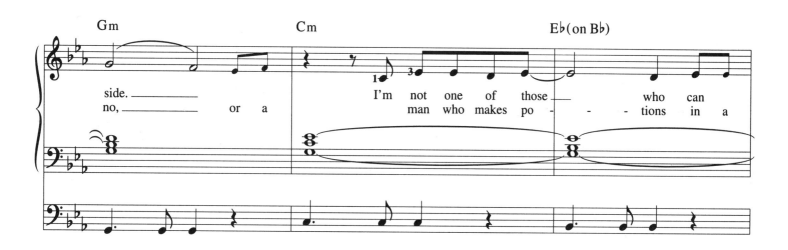

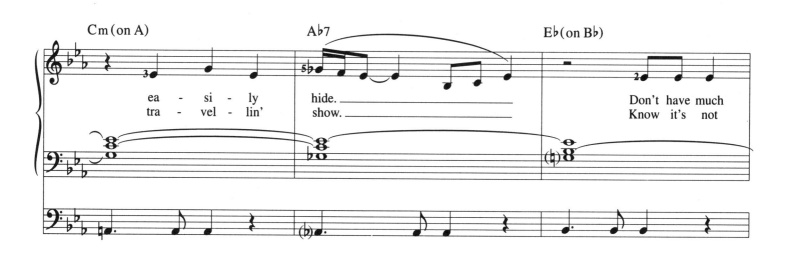

More Than A Woman

Words & Music by Barry Gibb, Robin Gibb & Maurice Gibb

Upper: trumpet
Lower: flutes
Pedal: bass guitar
Drums: disco (or rock)

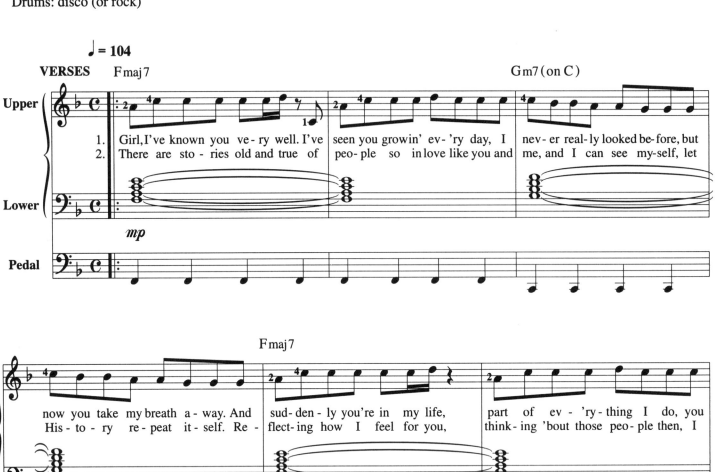

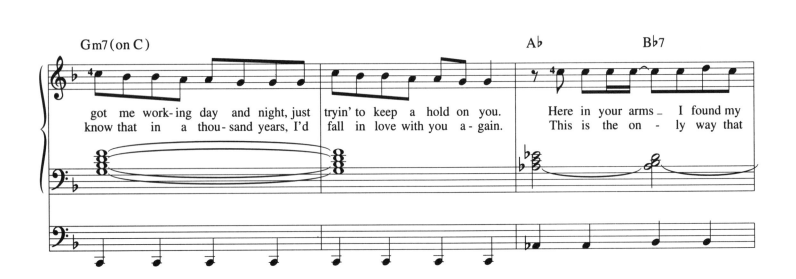

With You I'm Born Again

Words by Carol Conners
Music by David Shire

Upper: oboe
Lower: flutes
Pedal: 16' + 8'
Drums: waltz

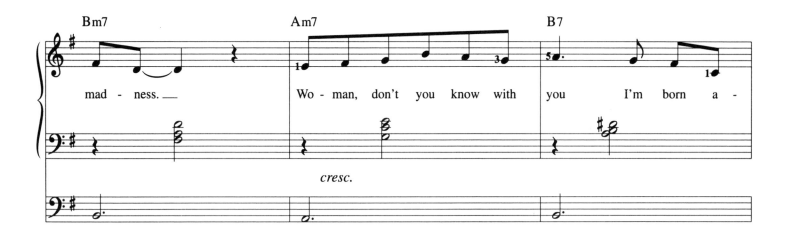

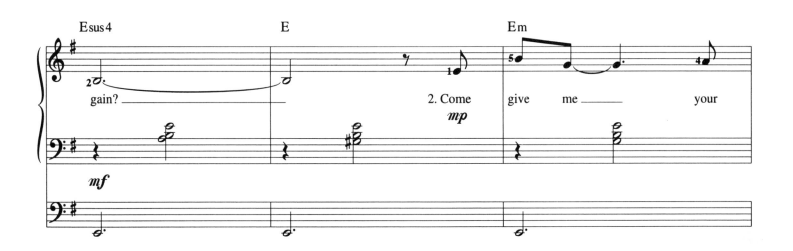

sweet - ness, ___ now there's you there is no weak - ness. ___

Wo - man, don't you know with you I'm born a - gain? ___

cresc. *mf*

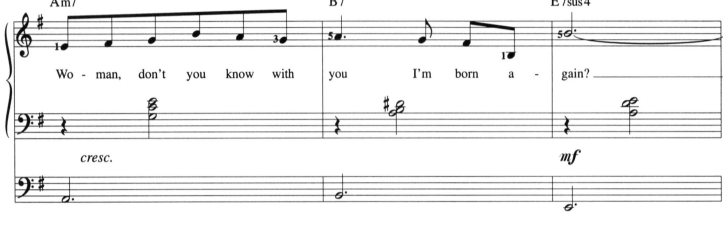

INTERLUDE

Upper: to clarinet

— I was half, not whole, in

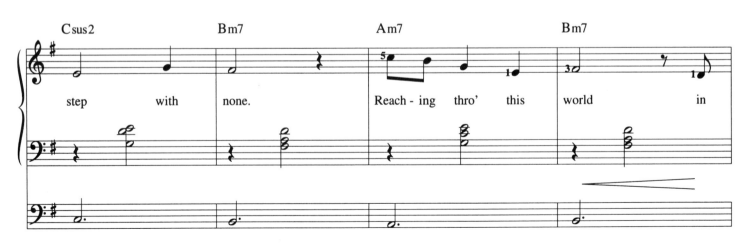

step with none. Reach - ing thro' this world in

My Love

Words & Music by McCartney

Upper: vibraphone
Lower: flutes
Pedal: bass guitar
Drums: 8 beat

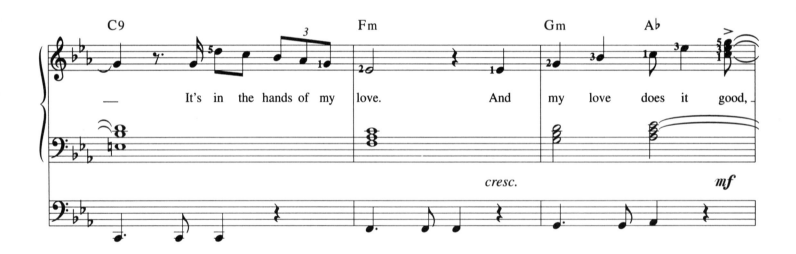

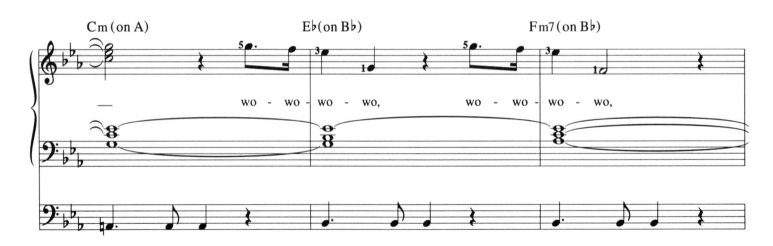

44

If Not For You

Words & Music by Bob Dylan

Upper: guitar
Lower: flutes + piano
Pedal: bass guitar
Drums: rock

With-out your love, I'd be no-where at all, I'd be lost if not for

you, and you know it's true.

3. If not for you

clue, and it would-n't ring

true, if not for you.

She Believes In Me

Words & Music by Steve Gibb

Upper: piano
Lower: flutes
Pedal: bass guitar
Drums: 8 beat

Unchained Melody

Music by Alex North
Words by Hy Zaret

Upper: saxophone
Lower: flutes
Pedal: 8'
Drums: 8 beat

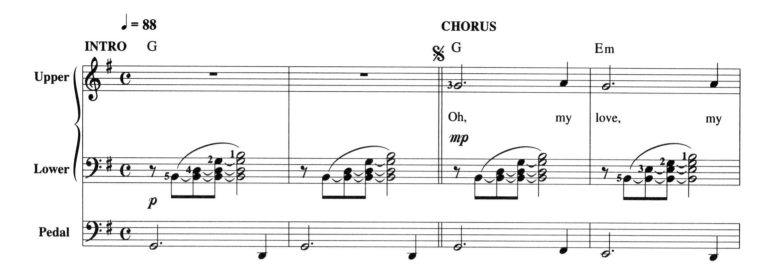

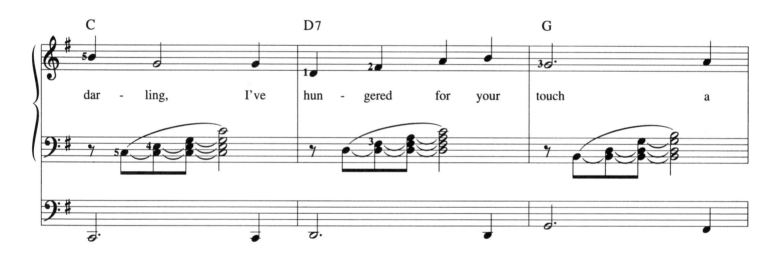

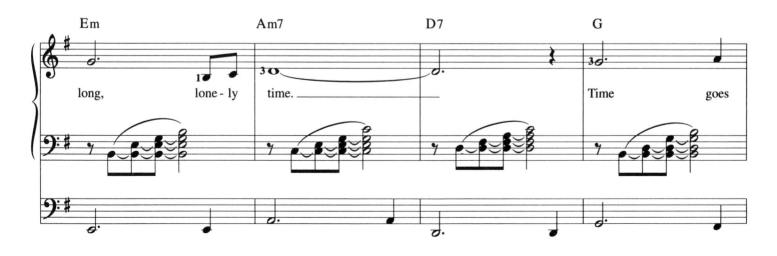

INTERLUDE

I Believe

Words & Music by Ervin Drake, Irvin Graham, Jimmy Shirl & Al Stillman

Upper: clarinet
Lower: flutes + piano
Pedal: bass guitar
Drums: slow rock

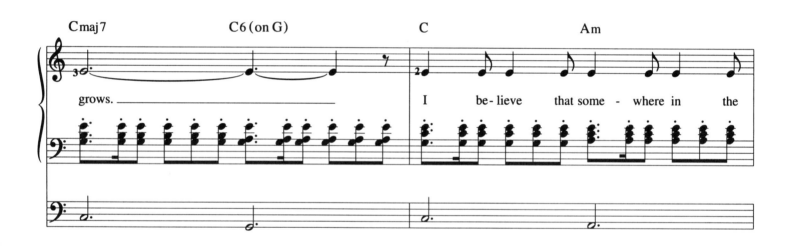

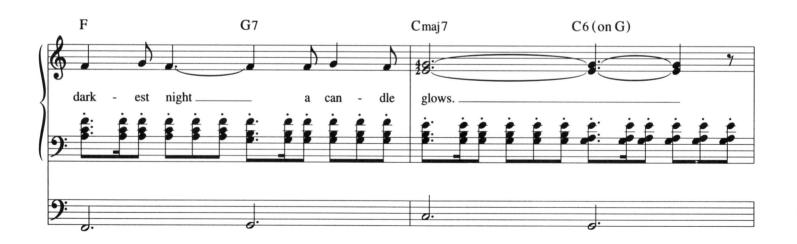

Love So Right

Words & Music by Barry Gibb, Robin Gibb & Maurice Gibb

Upper: flute
Lower: flutes
Pedal: bass guitar
Drums: 8 beat

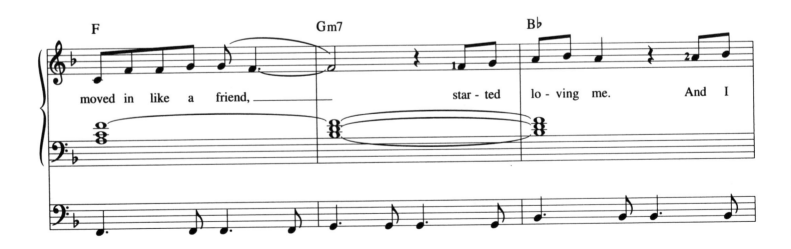

60

Goodnight Girl

Words & Music by Graeme Clark, Tom Cunningham, Neil Mitchell & Marti Pellow

Upper: guitar
Lower: flutes
Pedal: bass guitar
Drums: 8 beat

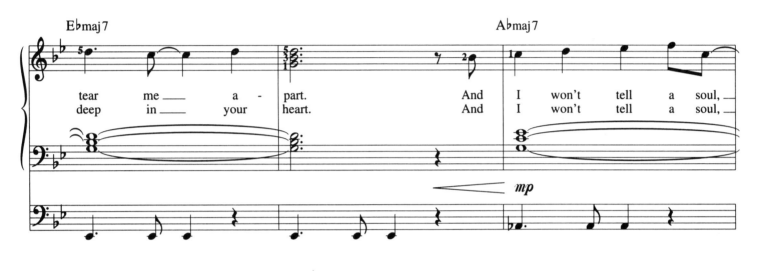

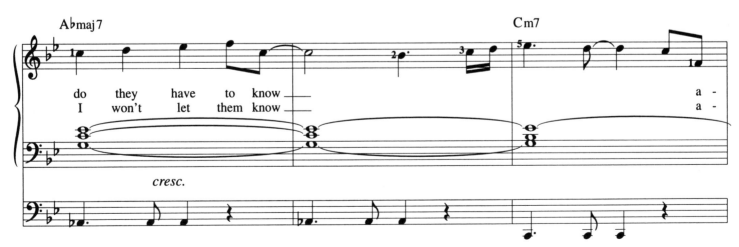

Stay Another Day

Words & Music by Mortimer, Kean & Hawken

Upper: clarinet
Lower: flutes
Pedal: bass guitar
Drums: 8 beat

Always

Words & Music by Jonathan Lewis, David Lewis & Wayne Lewis

Upper: oboe + strings
Lower: flutes
Pedal: bass guitar
Drums: 8 beat

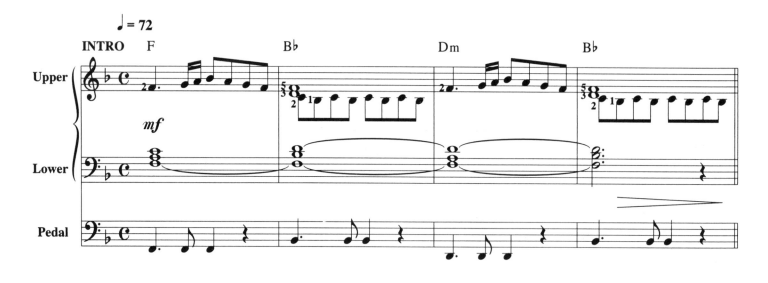

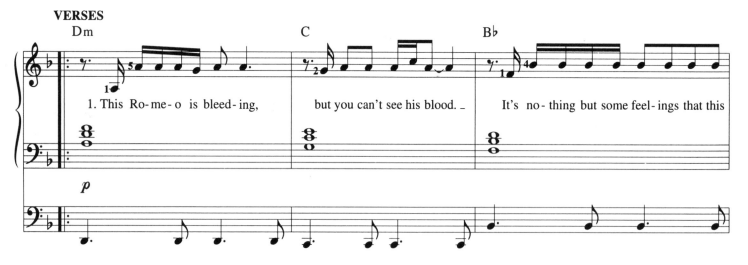

you see I've al-ways been a fight-er but with-out you I give up. ___ Now I can't sing a love song like the

way it's meant to be, ___ well I guess I'm not that good a-ny-more, ___ but ba-by, that's just me. ___ Yeah,

CHORUS

I will love ___ you, ba - by, ___ al - ways, and

I'll be there ___ for - ev - er and ___ a day, ___ al - ways.

Upper: oboe to flute

71

Verse 2

Now your pictures that you left behind
Are just memories of a different life,
Some that made us laugh, some that made us cry,
One that made you have to say goodbye.
What I'd give to run my fingers through your hair,
To touch your lips, to hold you near.
When you say your prayers
Try to understand, I've made mistakes, I'm just a man.
When he holds you close, when he pulls you near,
When he says the words you've been needing to hear,
I'll wish I was him, 'cause those words are mine,
To say to you till the end of time.

Love Is All Around

Words & Music by Reg Presley

Upper: brass ensemble
Lower: flutes
Pedal: bass guitar
Drums: 8 beat

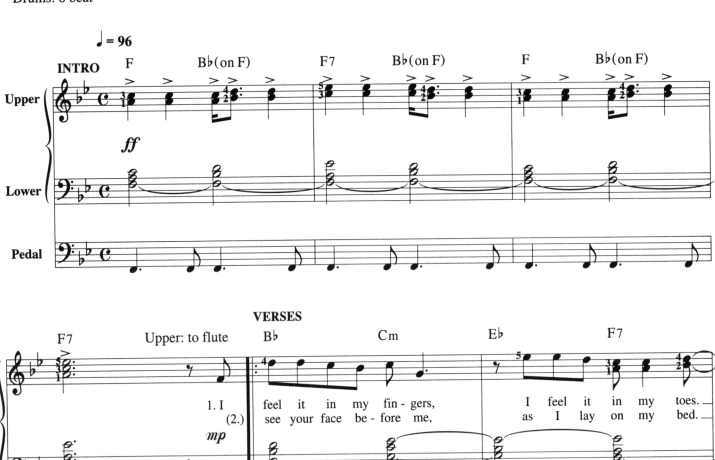

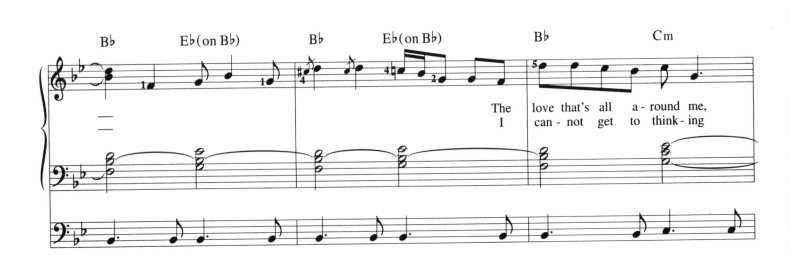

INTERLUDE

You know I love you, I al-ways __ will, __ my mind's made up by the

way that I feel. __ There's no be-gin - ning, there'll be no __ end, __ 'cause

on my __ love __ you can de - pend. __ Upper: to flute 2. I

Got to keep it mo-ving! 3. It's

76

How Deep Is Your Love

Words & Music by Barry Gibb, Robin Gibb & Maurice Gibb

Upper: vibraphone
Lower: flutes + piano
Pedal: bass guitar
Drums: rock

down, when they all should let us be. We be-

long to you and me.